SCOTCH IN MINIATURE

A Collector's Guide
by
Alan Keegan

*New and revised
edition*

Illustrations: Mairi Hedderwick

**Northern Books from
Famedram**

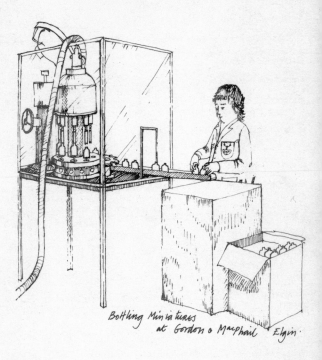

Bottling Miniatures at Gordon o Macphail Elgin.

Printed and published in Scotland for Northern Books by
Famedram Publishers Limited, Gartocharn, Dunbartonshire.

Contents

Introduction

SINCE THE original publication of this book, there have
been many changes in the world of Whisky Miniatures.
There has been a notable increase in the number of single
malt whiskies available in miniature form. This is good
news for the collector and most welcome to the
connoisseur whose tasting experience may thereby be
widened without commitment to a full 75 cl bottle.

There has been a significant increase in the use of
miniature whiskies for promotional use, especially by
hotels and stores. There have also been more miniatures
issued to commemorate particular events; since these
should be limited in number, they will form a prized part
of any collection. Examples are the three (now
unobtainable) miniatures issued for the Scottish Licensed
Trade Association in 1981 (Royal Wedding), 1982
(Inverness) and 1983 (Aviemore). At least one wedding
has been commemorated on a miniature label.

Collectors with overseas connections will have noted
some handsome miniatures issued for promotion of
Scotch Whisky brands in overseas markets; for example,
Grant's Royal, Buchanan's "de luxe" and Royal Ages.
On the home market, too, there has been some welcome
improvement in presentation: more miniatures are boxed
(Glengarioch, Glenfarclas, Laphroaig) and the 'true
miniature' of Dunhill Old Master whisky is the most
handsome issue since Dimple Haïg.

A less welcome development is the proliferation of
miniature labels issued for their own sake, without
significant relevance to the whisky contained in the bottle.
One can only repeat the message in the section 'Label
Printing': most collectors will find sufficient scope for
their hobby among whiskies issued for good reasons (as
samples, as commemorative souvenirs or as promotional
material) and will be suitably wary of labels that seem to
have been printed only because there are collectors about!

May 1986

Acknowledgements

In writing this book, I have been helped by many friends in the whisky trade. In particular, David Urquhart of Gordon and MacPhail has been of great assistance when compiling the lists. It has been possible to check the stocks of only a selected number of retailers, so that readers may find that other miniatures are available locally.

I am grateful to Jack Richmond of Newtonmore, who has cheerfully permitted me to plunder his great store of knowledge of all aspects of Scotch Whisky.

My wife has suffered long while I struggled with fact and syntax. To her and to the spouses of all committed whisky people, whether bottle collectors or imbibers, this book is dedicated.

In revising the lists, I have been helped by a number of collectors, but some useful suggestions must await a more radical re-writing.

I am specially grateful to Alex Barclay for his generous help in updating the malt whisky lists.

· Caol Ila ·

Some History

The first written record of a spirit distilled in Scotland from malted barley was in 1494 but the earlier story of *usquebaugh* is unknown. It seems likely that knowledge of distilling came to Scotland from Ireland some centuries before that first record.

The first 'named' whisky was Ferintosh, from the village in Ross-shire where Duncan Forbes of Culloden earned government protection for a distilling operation in the late seventeenth century.

During the eighteenth century high taxation encouraged illicit distilling, particularly in the remoter districts of the counties of Banff and Inverness. The modern era of the whisky industry dates from 1823 when the Whisky Act made legal distilling more profitable than smuggling. Shortly afterwards a practical continuous still was patented, leading to the growth of the big Lowland grain distilleries. Later in the nineteenth century the absence from the English market of brandy through decimation of the French vineyards opened the way for the expansion of whisky sales.

In the middle years of the nineteenth century, grain and malt distillers sold their products independently. The idea of mixing different whiskies was first applied to malts, e.g. in Usher's 'Old Vatted Glenlivet'; from this, it was only a short step to mixing the cheap (but bland) grain whiskies with the more expensive flavourful malts. Soon, the great whisky barons, Haig, Buchanan, Dewar and Mackie, who were entrepreneurs of blended whiskies rather than distillers, took over the destinies of the Scotch whisky trade.

Casks, sometimes of capacity as little as five gallons, were the first containers of whisky. Merchants sold to dram shops and inns in large stoneware jars which were often protected by an outer basket of wicker. The dram shops catered for the 'carry out' trade by filling customer's own flagons or jugs. It was only late in the nineteenth century, when the big blending houses developed their own brand names, that the bottling of whisky became common.

Even in the earliest days of the trade it is likely that small bottles were filled as samples. There is a record of the finding of a labelled medicine type bottle of Glen Grant under the floor of the town hall in Rothes, apparently left there by the builders in 1900. The issuing of miniature bottles as we know them developed in the United States. Triffon (see p. 80) lists a miniature Bourbon Whiskey named Fulton dating from about 1910.

The first miniatures of Scotch Whisky seem also to have been issued for the American market, as part of the great promotional drive that followed upon the repeal of prohibition in 1933.

The earliest miniatures were corked and sealed in various ways. The Black and White miniature from this time was accompanied by a wire corkscrew to facilitate access to the contents.

Collecting Miniature Whiskies

An interest in miniature Scotch whiskies often comes from a desire to collect and display them, rather than from the expectation of enjoying their contents. The collector, faced with a long list of available miniatures, may be discouraged if his budget is small and space for display is limited. Fortunately, there is scope for specialising, so that a collection of as few as a dozen miniatures can have real significance, if buying has been purposeful.

If the collector decides to concentrate on malt whiskies he might start with a representative from each of the tasting areas suggested on page 61. The collection may then be built up, as quickly as funds and space allow, in this sort of way:

1. One example from each tasting area. Target: 9.
2. A sample from each distillery in an area. Target 2 - 26.
3. One miniature from each distillery. Target 84.
4. A miniature for each proof and age. Target 120.
5. Every variation in label and bottle. Target 175+.

It is less easy to break down blended whiskies into classifications, but specialisation is possible. For example:

6. Collect 'true' miniatures only. (See page 12.)
7. Collect only brands available in U.K. in standard bottles.
8. Collect on an historical basis, staring with the oldest surviving brand names. The first target would be Ushers, if you can still find an example, this being one of the disappearing miniatures (see page 15). The 'Top Fifteen' in a collection following these lines would be: Ushers, Vat 69, John Begg, Haig's, Johnnie Walker, Mackinlay's, Buchanan's, Dewar's, White Horse, Queen Anne, Long John, Teacher's, Bell's, Highland Queen, J & B Rare . . .

Other possibilities for specialising may be suggested by the topics covered in the pages that follow.

OBAN · BLACK & WHITE · DEWARS DE LUXE · ARGYLL · THE BALVENIE · BALVENIE PURE MALT · THE ANTIQUARY · DIMPLE · WHITE HEATHER · THE GLENLIVET · HOUSE OF COMMONS · CHEQUERS · FAMOUS GROUSE · EATON'S

Enjoying Miniature Whiskies

The collector who is also a whisky drinker, particularly one who is fond of malts, has an easier basis for specialising; he can restrict his collecting to miniatures of the whiskies he has sampled. He is less likely to share the view of many collectors who are reluctant to display empty miniatures.

Specialisation involves research and this will help to give point to what otherwise might be a sterile process of mere acquisition. It is a recurrent theme of this book that whether miniatures are bought as samples for tasting or as collector's pieces, the enjoyment of the process will be the greater if the purchaser is interested in the special character of the whisky as well as in the container and the label.

Definitions

MALT WHISKY is produced in pot stills, using malted barley as the base material. The process is intermittent, one batch being completed before the next is put in the still. Modern distilleries may be highly mechanised but they follow closely on traditional methods, so that each distillery produces a whisky of uniquely distinctive character. When bottled on its own, the product of a distillery is a **single** malt.

VATTED MALTS are blendings of the products of two or more malt distilleries. Bottlers do not use the word 'vatted' on their labels, preferring the less specific terms 'pure malt' or '100% malt'.

GRAIN WHISKY is produced by a continuous process in patent stills. A fermented 'wash' of grain (usually maize, but with some malted barley) is fed into the still and the alcohol is collected at the end of the process. The patent still operates at a higher temperature than the pot still and is more efficient but much flavour is lost, so that the whiskies from the different grain distilleries have little distinctive individuality. The products of both malt and grain distilleries must be matured for three years before the spirit may legally be termed whisky.

BLENDED WHISKY contains both malt and grain whiskies. The proportion of each depends on the requirements of the bottler regarding cost and quality. Standard blends usually contain about 30% malt whiskies; a de luxe blend will probably have a higher proportion of malt but a cheap brand will certainly have much more grain.

11

True Miniature

In this book, a 'true' miniature is one which fairly reproduces on a small scale the appearance of a standard . (75 cl) bottle. There is a special satisfaction to be had from possessing these replicas, especially when the shape of the larger bottle or the design of its label are pleasing or unusual.

For reasons of economy, miniatures tend now to come in standard shapes and some issues of unusual shape are no longer to be found. An example of this is Crawford's three star, whose distinctive brown bottle, true to the original, has been replaced with a clear flat (airline) miniature. Two other distinctive 'true' miniatures that have been withdrawn are Teacher's and Crawford's Five Star. Oban and Something Special are two 'decanter' style miniatures that may soon disappear.

For the export market there seems to be a counter movement, perhaps influenced by excellent presentation of miniatures of Japanese Whisky.

Some of the bottlings by James Buchanan & Co. offer an interesting study in the field of true miniatures. The 75 cl bottles of Black & White, Strathconon and House of Commons have distinctive angular shoulders, while Buchanan's Blend is in the standard (round shouldered) bottle. Among the miniatures, only House of Commons has the angular shoulders, so that we should count only it and Buchanan's Blend among the true miniatures.

12

Miniature Bottles, Red Lead and Painting on a Small Scale

It is an interesting and surprising fact that, in its original meaning, the word 'miniature' had nothing at all to do with smallness. The present usage is influenced by the similarity in sound to the Latin word for smaller (minor) and smallest (minimus).

The word 'miniature' comes from the Italian *miniate*, meaning to paint with minium or red lead. This substance was used as a base for the intricate work of illuminating manuscripts. The term 'miniatura' was subsequently applied to intricately painted small portraits and to any painting done on a small scale. It was an easy step from this usage to the present dictionary definition of 'miniature' as "a small or reduced copy of anything".

Proof

Whisky contains water as well as alcohol. When we speak of 'proof', we are concerned with the relative amount of water in the whisky.

In an early test of proof, alcohol was mixed with gunpowder and a match applied: the alcohol was under proof if the mixture failed to ignite, over proof if it exploded and 'proof' if it burned with a steady blue flame. When strength came to be measured more scientifically with a hydrometer, the amount over or under proof was measured in degrees, 'proof' being 100° in the old British 'Sikes' system.

Since 1980, when Britain subscribed to the International Organisation of Legal Metrology, we have adopted the continental (Gay Lusac) system, in which the alcohol content is expressed as a percentage of the total volume of the spirit at 20°C. Under the Sikes system, standard bottling of whisky was at 70° proof. The equivalent today is 40°GL or 40% vol. In terms of the measurement used in America, this is 80° proof (US).

Malt whisky is normally distilled at between 115° and 120°. It is slightly reduced in strength before being placed in casks for maturation at about 110° (63% vol.). Since alcohol evaporates more quickly than water, the maturing whisky gradually loses strength, but it is normally necessary to add water before bottling.

Unusually, Balvenie under the 'As We Get It' label, is bottled at the strength it comes from the maturing cask; in the case of the current miniature, bottling was at 108.6° proof or 62% alcohol by volume. This is the highest proof of any whisky available in bottle.

IOLM/GL (%)	Sikes ° Proof	American ° Proof	
40	70	80	Standard strength, U.K. market.
43	75	86	Export strength. Standard U.S.
46	80	92	
50	87.5	100	
57	100	114	Strongest Blend Min. (Glen Calder)
60	105	120	Glenfarclas, Highland Fusilier
62	108.6	124	Strongest Miniature (see above)
100	173.35	200	Pure (absolute) Alcohol

Disappearing Miniatures

All the miniature blended whiskies listed were available at the time of writing, though some can be purchased only in a few specialist shops. However, supply is sometimes doubtful and if a miniature disappears from the shelves, the chances are that it will not reappear. This is particularly applicable to miniatures issued by the major whisky companies, which are always linked to promotional or other commercial considerations.

The fickle nature of the market is illustrated by the following list of miniature bottlings which have disappeared from the shops within the last few years: MacGregor's, Macleay Duff, Talisker, Cawdor Castle, Diner's Club, Crawford's 5 star. Most of the original Cadenhead bottlings. Macallan and Glenfarclas from Tartanpack range.

 Occasionally there are surprise reappearances. One miniature which had been off the market for some time but which became available again recently, is Dimple Haig. This splendid miniature was first issued in the thirties and has been the starting point for many collections. It has appeared in several forms, some having the mesh of wire that distinguished the original larger bottle. The present, temporary, availability of this miniature follows the re-introduction of Dimple into the U.K. market as a 12 year old whisky; the miniatures held for promotional purposes had the old labelling and were released on the market, to the benefit of today's collector. A limited number with the 12 year old labelling has also been released.

Prior to the introduction of Glenordie Malt, Dewar's 12 year old Pure Malt miniature was available temporarily and a few may still be found.

Label Language and the Quality of Blends

The description on the label of a miniature blended whisky may not be a reliable guide to the contents. Details of strength and capacity often go unrecorded. There may even be a better known parent company behind the name of the bottler.

Some whisky companies show a remarkable want of modesty when describing their product. The most ordinary blend is 'special', 'choice' or 'the finest'. A product declared on the label to be 'old', 'rare' or even both old and rare, may be quite young for a whisky. We come to accept these terms as embroidery.

The description 'de luxe' is more reliable, this being applied by whisky companies to their premium (as distinct from their standard) blends. A similar use is made of the word 'reserve'.

Some blends carry an indication of age on the label. When this occurs, every constituent whisky in the blend, grain as well as malt, must by law have attained that age at the time of bottling. Although many premium blends declare themselves to be twelve years old, absence of a stated age does not mean that the blend lacks mature malts or that the whisky is inferior to a 12 year old. Other factors that determine the character of a blend are the proportion of malt whisky to grain and the quality of the constituent malts.

The cost of a blend will be increased if the blender uses 'crack' malts (Cragganmore, Glen Grant, Glenlivet, Macallan) or others from the top category, rather than cheaper, less effective malts. In the final analysis, it is not the words on the label but the taste of the contents that will determine how well a blend sells.

Blended Whisky Miniatures — Explanation of Lists

The blended whiskies listed on the following pages are those miniatures that were available for purchase in the U.K. at the time of writing. Many are are to be found only in specialist shops (see page 77).

Entry in italics indicates the miniature has been discontinued and may be hard to find.

NAME OF BLEND	This is the name most prominent on the label. The name of the bottler is given only when it is part of the name of the blend.
DETAILS	**Age** is shown if it is on the label. **Proof** is noted only when the label indicates that strength is different from standard 40%.
SHAPE	T True miniature (see page 14) Ro Round — standard tall round Rd Round — dumpy shape Sq Square — tall; also known as 'Irish square' Sd Square — dumpy shape Fa Flat — standard 'airline', rounded edges Fl Flask — curved, hip flask style Fs Flat — rectangular in section Tri Triangular in section Dec Decanter or decorative bottle Var Issued in various formats
COLOUR	Cl Clear Bk Black Br Brown Gr Green
NOTES	TP 'Tartanpak' format of Gordon & Macphail DL Issued by Douglas Laing & Co. GS Issued by George Strachan Ltd. LB Issued by Lambert Brothers.

Blend Miniatures

Name of Blend	Details	Shape & Colour		Note
Abbot's Choice	–	Br	Fa	Boxed
Aboyne Games	–	Cl	Ro	GS
Ainslie's Royal Edinburgh	–	Br	Fa	Boxed
Ambassador de Luxe	T	Gr	Ro	
Ambassador Royal	12 yo 43%	T	Gr	Ro
Ancestor	T	Gr	Sd	
Antiquary	T	Cl	Dec	
Argyll	T	Cl	Sq	
Atlas de Luxe	–	Gr	Ro	LB
Auchinloch	–	Cl	Var	DL
Auld Curlers	–	Cl	Ro	GS
Auld Rorie	–	Gr	Ro	LB
Avonside	8 yo 40% –	Cl	Fl	TP
Avonside	8 yo 57% –	Cl	Fl	TP

Dewar's Ancestor is a handsome
miniature, true to the original. It is available
in several overseas markets but its present
appearance on the home market is limited,
being available (as is Dewar's Malt) only
as part of a family pack (see page 33).

18

Blend Miniatures

Name of Blend	Details	Shape & Colour			Notes
Balgownie		–	Cl	Ro	
Ballantine's	12 yo 43%	T	Cl	Fs	
Ballantine's		T	Br	Fs	
B.B. (Gold)		–	Cl	Var	DL
B.B. (Red)		–	Cl	Var	DL
Bell's		–	Cl	Dec	
Bell's	12 yo		Cl	Ro	
Ben Alder		T	Cl	Ro	Also TP
Beneagles (Golden)		T	Cl	Ro	
Ben Roland		–	Cl	Ro	
Big T	43%	T	Cl	Ro	
Black & White		T	Cl	Ro	Also Fl & Fa
Black Bottle		T	Gr	Dec	Was Ro & Fa
Black Colt		–	Cl	Ro	LB
Black Douglas		–	Cl	Var	DL
Boulevard		–	Gr	Ro	LB
Brodie's Supreme		T	Gr	Ro	
Buchanan's Blend		T	Cl	Ro	
Buchanan's Reserve		T	Cl	Dec	
Buckie Lugger		–	Cl	Ro	GS

Benn A'Chleibh and 10 other bens have been issued under Lambert Brothers' 'Munros' series.

Some distinguished true miniatures are illustrated on these pages. Other bottles of distinctive shape that are reproduced in the miniature form are: Ancestor, Glayva, Old Parr, President, Something Special, Vat 69, White Heather and Dunhill.

Blend Miniatures

Name of Blend	Details	Shape & Colour			Notes
Cairns (Eadie Cairns)		T	Cl	Sq	
Campbeltown Loch		T	Gr	Ro	
Carlton	5 yo	–	Cl	Fa	
Catto's	43%	T	Gr	Ro	
Chequers		T	Gr	Ro	Also flagon
Chivas Regal	12 yo 43%	T	Cl	Rd	
Clan Blend		–	Cl	Ro	Also TP
Clan Campbell	5 yo 43%	T	Gr	Ro	Also Fa
Cluny		–	Cl	Fa	
Clydebank		–	Cl	Var	DL
Cotton's No. 1		–	Cl	Ro	LB
Crawford's ***		–	Cl	Fa	Was Br Rd
Craw's Nest		T	Cl	Ro	
Cream of Glenlivet		–	Cl	Fa	
Cream of the Barley			Cl	Rd	Also Dec
Crinan Canal Water		T	Cl	Ro	
Crown of Scotland		T	Gr	Ro	
Cutty Sark		T	Gr	Ro	

Cream of the Barley may occasionally be found in the distinctive 'decanter' format of the 75 cl bottle.

Cream of Glenlivet has an unusual label, being lozenge shaped. This whisky miniature is unusual also in that not only is it bottled in England, but also, along with 'Finest Liquour', it has the name of a brewery (Park Brewery, Wolverhampton) on its label. Gairloch is another miniature bottled in England.

Blend Miniatures

Name of Blend	Details	Shape & Colour			Notes
Dalmeny		–	Cl	Fa	
Dewar's White Label		T	Cl	Ro	Also Fa
Dice		–	Cl	Var	DL
Dimple (Haig's)	12 yo	T	Cl	Dec	
Director's Choice		–	Gr	Ro	LB
DL 13		–	Cl	Sq	DL
Deerstalker		–	Cl	Ro	LB
Dunhill Old Master		T	Br	Dec	
Eaton's		–	Cl	Var	DL
Eight Fellows		–	Cl	Var	DL
Falcon		–	Cl	Ro	GS
Falklands		–	Cl	Fa	
Famous Grouse		T	Cl	Ro	
Findlater's		T	Cl	Ro	
Finest Liquour		–	Cl	Fa	
First Lord	43%	–	Gr	Ro	
Four Seasons		–	Cl	Fa	

Collectors who are addicted to seeking out label variations may like to know that there are no less than 63 different **current** versions for Dewar's White Label miniatures. Multiply this by the number of widely distributed whisky brands and double that again to allow for discontinued versions, and one reaches a target figure that could turn a collector to specialising in empty malt miniatures. If he remains undeterred, then his addiction is surely incurable.

Blend Miniatures

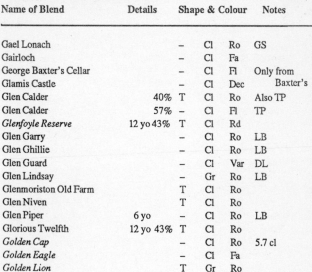

Name of Blend	Details		Shape & Colour		Notes
Gael Lonach		–	Cl	Ro	GS
Gairloch		–	Cl	Fa	
George Baxter's Cellar		–	Cl	Fl	Only from
Glamis Castle		–	Cl	Dec	Baxter's
Glen Calder	40%	T	Cl	Ro	Also TP
Glen Calder	57%	–	Cl	Fl	TP
Glenfoyle Reserve	12 yo 43%	T	Cl	Rd	
Glen Garry		–	Cl	Ro	LB
Glen Ghillie		–	Cl	Ro	LB
Glen Guard		–	Cl	Var	DL
Glen Lindsay		–	Gr	Ro	LB
Glenmoriston Old Farm		T	Cl	Ro	
Glen Niven		T	Cl	Ro	
Glen Piper	6 yo	–	Cl	Ro	LB
Glorious Twelfth	12 yo 43%	T	Cl	Ro	
Golden Cap		–	Cl	Ro	5.7 cl
Golden Eagle		–	Cl	Fa	
Golden Lion		T	Gr	Ro	

Glenmoriston Old Farm, with its effective label design, has been re-issued but with a glossy label that is less distinctive than the original 'parchment' effect.

Golden Cap is about 2 cms taller than the standard round miniature. Thistle Blend may also be found in this format.

Blend Miniatures

Name of Blend	Details	Shape & Colour		Note
Gold Label (Salisbury's)	–	Cl	Fa	
Grand McNish	–	Cl	Ro	3 cl
Grand Scot	–	Cl	Fa	
Grant's Standfast	T	Cl	Tri	
Grant's	12 yo	T	Cl	Tri	
Grant's Royal	T	Cl	Tri	
Grendel's	–	Cl	Fa	DL
Grendel's	12 yo	–	Cl	Fa	DL
Grog Blossom	–	Cl	Ro	GS
Haig's	–	Cl	Fa	Was Br
Hamilton's	–	Cl	Var	DL
Hankey Bannister	T	Cl	Sq	
Harrod's de Luxe	–	Gr	Ro	Available only from Harrod's
Hart's	–	Cl	Var	DL
Headington	–	Gr	Ro	LB
Heather	–	Cl	Ro	LB
Heebie Jeebies	–	Cl	Ro	GS

Grand McNish and Old Smuggler, both in small 3 cl bottles and both export brands, have found their way onto the UK market in small quantities.

Blend Miniatures

Name of Blend	Details	Shape & Colour			Notes
Hielanman	8 yo	–	Cl	Ro	
Hielanman		T	Gr	Ro	
Highlander		–	Cl	Fa	
Highland Fuselier 25th Anniv.		–	Cl	Ro	GM also TP
H.B.C.		–	Cl	Fa	
Highland Mist		T	Cl	Ro	
Highland Mist	8 yo	T	Cl	Ro	
Highland Queen		T	Cl	Ro	
Highland Star		–	Cl	Fa	
Hopetoun House		–	Cl	Dec	Watch Glass
House of Commons	12 yo	T	Cl	Ro	On sale at H of C only
House of Lords	8 yo	T	Cl	Sd	Also Fl
House of Peers		–	Cl	Var	
House of Strachan		–	Cl	Ro	GS
House of Stuart		T	Gr	Ro	
Howtowdie		–	Cl	Ro	LB

Unlike the House of Commons, the upper chamber of parliament does not have its own restricted miniature bottling. Both House of Lords and House of Peers are proprietory brands freely available in shops.

Hielanman carries a picture of a Music Hall Highlander, sturdy, bearded and kilted, with a glass in one hand and a Harry Lauder stick in the other.

Blend Miniatures

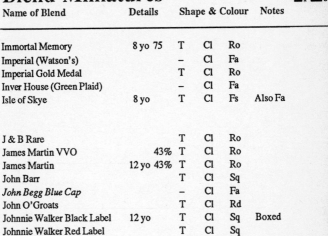

Name of Blend	Details	Shape	& Colour		Notes
Immortal Memory	8 yo 75	T	Cl	Ro	
Imperial (Watson's)		–	Cl	Fa	
Imperial Gold Medal		T	Cl	Ro	
Inver House (Green Plaid)		–	Cl	Fa	
Isle of Skye	8 yo	T	Cl	Fs	Also Fa
J & B Rare		T	Cl	Ro	
James Martin VVO	43%	T	Cl	Ro	
James Martin	12 yo 43%	T	Cl	Ro	
John Barr		T	Cl	Sq	
John Begg Blue Cap		–	Cl	Fa	
John O'Groats		T	Cl	Rd	
Johnnie Walker Black Label	12 yo	T	Cl	Sq	Boxed
Johnnie Walker Red Label		T	Cl	Sq	

John O'Groats is newly available in this country, being an old established export blend of the Drambuie Liquer Co. Among scotches, it is unusual in that the label describes the contents as '*Scots* Liqueur Whisky'.

Blend Miniatures

Name of Blend	Details	Shape & Colour		Notes
Kentshire	–	Cl	Var	DL
Kindrochit Castle	–	Cl	Ro	GS
King Edgar	–	Cl	Fa	
King Henry VIII	–	Cl	Fa	
King of Scots	–	Cl	Var	DL
King's Ransom	T	Cl	Sd	Also Fl
King William IV	T	Cl	Ro	
Lambert's Favourite	–	Cl	Ro	LB
Langside	–	Cl	Fa	DL also Sq
Lang's Supreme	T	Cl	Ro	
L.B.E. Black Label	–	Cl	Ro	LB
L.B.E. Red Label	–	Cl	Ro	LB
Leland's	–	Cl	Ro	LB
Liverpool Garden Festival	–	Cl	Ro	
Lochlomac	–	Cl	Var	DL
Logan de Luxe	T	Cl	Fs	
Lombard's	–	Cl	Fa	
Long John	–	Cl	Fa	Was Ro
Lord Douglas	T	Cl	Ro	
Lord Salisbury	–	Cl	Fa	

Names like 'Leland's', 'Murnanes', 'Rochambeau' and 'Headington' sound rather odd on a list of blended Scotch whiskies. These are, in fact, the names of stores or liquour shops in the US, for whom special labels have been issued.

Blend Miniatures

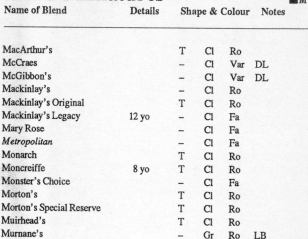

Name of Blend	Details	Shape & Colour		Notes
MacArthur's		T Cl	Ro	
McCraes	–	Cl	Var	DL
McGibbon's	–	Cl	Var	DL
Mackinlay's	–	Cl	Ro	
Mackinlay's Original		T Cl	Ro	
Mackinlay's Legacy	12 yo	– Cl	Fa	
Mary Rose		– Cl	Fa	
Metropolitan		– Cl	Fa	
Monarch		T Cl	Ro	
Moncreiffe	8 yo	T Cl	Ro	
Monster's Choice		– Cl	Fa	
Morton's		T Cl	Ro	
Morton's Special Reserve		T Cl	Ro	
Muirhead's		T Cl	Ro	
Murnane's	–	Gr	Ro	LB

The 'Munros' series initiated by Lambert Brothers has 11
names, so far. There are 279 Munros (i.e. Scottish mountain
tops of 3,000 feet or more), listed in the *Munros Tables*
published by the Scottish Mountaineering Club.

Blend Miniatures

Name of Blend	Details	Shape & Colour			Notes
National Choice		T	Cl	Ro	
Noble Glen		–	Cl	Var	DL
Old Arthur		–	Cl	Fa	
Old Barrister		T	Cl	Ro	
Old Cobblers		–	Cl	Ro	GS
Old Court		T	Cl	Ro	
Old Highland Liqueur		–	Cl	Fa	LB
Old Inverness		T	Cl	Ro	
Old Mull		–	Cl	Fl	Boxed
Old Orkney		T	Cl	Ro	Also TP
Old Parr		T	Br	Dec	Boxed
Old Royal	15 yo 43%	–	Cl	Fa	
Old Scotia		–	Cl	Ro	LB
Old Smuggler		T	Cl	Ro	3 cl
Old Smuggler	12 yo	–	Cl	Ro	
Old Troon	5 yo	T	Cl	Ro	
Old Troon Royale		–	Cl	Ro	
OV 8		–	Cl	Fa	

A number of miniatures are not likely to be bought as souvenirs of Scotland; Nelson, for example, and King Henry VIII. Nor is National Choice likely to be selected for its Scottishness, since the label depicts Red Rum, three times Grand National winner.

Blend Miniatures

Name of Blend	Details	Shape & Colour			Notes
Pheasant Plucker		T	Cl	Ro	GS
Pig's Nose		–	Cl	Ro	
Pinwinnie	12 yo	–	Gr	Fa	Cloth Bag
Piper's		–	Cl	Ro	
President		T	Cl	Ro	
Prime Blend		–	Cl	Ro	LB
Prince Harry		–	Cl	Fa	
Prince Howard		–	Gr	Ro	LB
Putachieside		–	Cl	Ro	
Queen Anne		T	Cl	Ro	Was Gr Fa
Real MacKenzie		T	Cl	Ro	
Red Hackle		T	Cl	Ro	
Red Lion		–	Cl	Fa	
Robbie Burns		T	Br	Dec	
Rob Roy		T	Cl	Ro	
Rochambeau		–	Cl	Ro	LB
Ronson	5 yo	–	Cl	Sq	
Ronson	12 yo	–	Cl	Sq	
Royal Deeside		T	Cl	Ro	GS was Fa
Royal Wedding Commemorative		–	Cl	Fa	Also Fs and Watch Glass

Pig's Nose, Pheasant Plucker

These titles reflect, perhaps, the modern day urge to be outrageous. Amusing to some, but deplored by the many traditionalists in the whisky world who think such gimmicks unnecessary.

Pinwinnie is sold in a pretty cloth bag. Until recently it also came in a box which, because of its intricate shape, tended to tear on opening.

Blend Miniatures

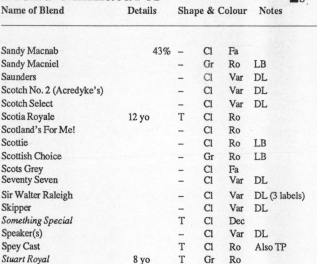

Name of Blend	Details	Shape & Colour		Notes
Sandy Macnab	43% –	Cl	Fa	
Sandy Macniel	–	Gr	Ro	LB
Saunders	–	Cl	Var	DL
Scotch No. 2 (Acredyke's)	–	Cl	Var	DL
Scotch Select	–	Cl	Var	DL
Scotia Royale	12 yo	T Cl	Ro	
Scotland's For Me!	–	Cl	Ro	
Scottie	–	Cl	Ro	LB
Scottish Choice	–	Gr	Ro	LB
Scots Grey	–	Cl	Fa	
Seventy Seven	–	Cl	Var	DL
Sir Walter Raleigh	–	Cl	Var	DL (3 labels)
Skipper	–	Cl	Var	DL
Something Special		T Cl	Dec	
Speaker(s)	–	Cl	Var	DL
Spey Cast		T Cl	Ro	Also TP
Stuart Royal	8 yo	T Gr	Ro	

Sir Walter Raleigh, like the other Douglas Laing bottlings, may
be found in several formats. This particular miniature also
appears with at least three quite different labels and in at least
four differently shaped bottles.

Blend Miniatures

Name of Blend	Details	Shape & Colour		Notes
Talisman	–	Cl	Fa	LB
Tammie	–	Cl	Ro	LB
Tax Collector	T	Cl	Ro	
Teacher's	–	Cl	Ro	
Teacher's 60	–	Cl	Ro	
Teviotdale	T	Gr	Ro	
Thane of Cawdor	–	Cl	Ro	Only at Cawdor Castle
Thistle	–	Cl	Ro	5 cl & 5.7 cl
Three Brothers	–	Gr	Ro	LB
Tinker's Dram	–	Cl	Ro	GS
Tobermory	T	Cl	Ro	
Turnberry Reserve	T	Cl	Ro	
Turnbull's Club	T	Gr	Ro	
Tuxedo	–	Cl	Var	DL

Teviotdale and Turnbull's Club are brands marketed, mostly overseas, by an established firm of whisky merchants who recently ceased to trade as retailers.

Tobermory is unusual in that both a blended whisky and a single malt are bottled in the name of the distillery, though this was previously known as Ledaig. The distillery is colourfully illustrated on the current label for the blend.

Blend Miniatures

Name of Blend	Details	Shape & Colour			Notes
Uisge Beatha		T	Cl	Ro	GS was Fa
Union Park			Cl	Ro	LB
Vat 69		T	Gr	Dec	
Vat 69 Reserve		T	Gr	Dec	
White Hart		–	Cl	Ro	Was Fa
White Heather	5 yo 43%	T	Cl	Sd	
White Heather	8 yo 43%	T	Cl	Sd	
White Horse		–	Cl	Fl	
Whiteinch		–	Cl	Var	DL
Whyte & Mackays		T	Cl	Rd	Also Fa
Whyte & Mackays de Luxe		–	Cl	Rd	
Whyte & Mackays	21 yo 43%				Plastic Flask
Wild Oats		–	Cl	Ro	GS
William Lawson		T	Gr	Ro	
Wimbledon		–	Cl	Fa	

The three Whyte & Mackay blends, along with Dalmore, Fettercairn and Tomintoul malts, can now be purchased as a set of miniature plastic flasks.

Family Packs

A number of companies have issued display packs to illustrate their product range. Some were prepared for export promotion and cannot be purchased but several can be found in shops, as indicated below.

Dewars

Fine Scotch Whiskies from the House of Dewars

Blend — Dewars
De luxe Blend — Ancestor
Vatted Malt — Dewars
or Malt — Glenordie

Black & White

With the compliments of James Buchanan & Co. Ltd.

Blend — Buchanan Blend
Blend — Black & White
De luxe Blend — Buchanan's Reserve

Not available

Macdonald & Muir

Fine Whiskies from Macdonald and Muir

Blend — Highland Queen
Malt — Glenmorangie
Malt — Glen Moray

Freely available in shops

Mackinlay's
The Mackinlay Family

Blend — Mackinlay's
De luxe Blend — Legacy
Malt — Isle of Jura

Not available

Bells

A Quality Gift from Scotland

Blend — Bells
Malt — Blair Athol
Malt — Dufftown

Freely available in shops

Glenlivet

The Glenlivet Distillers Ltd. Quartet

Blend — Queen Anne
De luxe Blend — Something Special
Malt — Glenlivet 12 yo
Malt — Glen Grant 12 yo

Recently withdrawn

Morrisons

Three Cheers from Stanley P. Morrison Ltd.

Blend — Rob Roy
Malt — Bowmore
Malt — Glengarioch

No longer available

Cumbrae Supply Co.

Scotches Blender Pack

Malt — Unnamed
Blend — Unnamed
Grain — Unnamed

From tourist shops

Variants

The lists of blended miniatures include only one entry for each brand and only major and recent variations are recorded in the notes. Many collectors will be content to have just one miniature for each brand. Others will want to acquire major variants while the fanatical few will consider even the smallest change in a label or bottle format a good reason for adding another miniature to their collection. It is not practical to attempt to list all variants but some of the things to look for are suggested in the following notes. Collectors who are keen to find out about all variants are advised to contact the Mini Bottle Club whose members regularly exchange information on this matter and similar subjects (see page 78).

BOTTLE SHAPES
Proprietory blends may be issued with the same label in a variety of formats, according to their intended use. Black and White, for example, has been issued as a tall round. a flask and a flat 'airline' miniature.

Miniatures issued by Douglas Laing & Co. are filled in several different bottles, according to the wishes of the particular customer.

Flat airline bottles were used for Aberlour malt when stocks of the familiar dumpy square bottle ran out.

DIFFERENT CAPS
Most such variations are probably casual. Tartanpak flasks can have gold, red or white caps. Glenmorangie has recently changed to a printed cap.

RE-DESIGNED LABELS
Many of the Tartanpak labels have recently been changed, as have the labels of Cairns, Dimple Haig, Glamis Castle, House of Stuart, Pig's Nose, Bladnoch and Tamnavulin.

PROOF AND CAPACITY
There are many instances of variations due to the introduction of metric measurements.

Shapely Bottles, Pretty Labels

That a miniature is pleasing to look at is as good a reason as any for choosing to buy it, if the contents are not likely to be consumed. However, if the miniature is a malt whisky and is intended for sampling, appearance should not be the deciding factor (otherwise we should grow tired of tasting Oban, Aberlour VOHM and Glenmorangie from a drum.)

The labels on many miniatures are scaled-down versions of those on the 75 cl bottle and this is good if both containers have the same general shape. However, if for example, the miniature is a flask while the label was deisgned for a standard round bottle. the combination can be unattractive. Compare the appearance of the tall round miniatures issued by Gordon & Macphail with the Tartanpak miniatures with the same label.

There has been a trend recently towards lighter coloured labels on whisky miniatures. Glen Moray, Lang's, Glengoyne and Queen Anne have all received tan (whisky coloured?) labels in place of black. Balvenie has lost its black 'leather-look' label, in favour of a very unusual grey one. The combination of this label and the bottle shape — the 3 cl capacity suggests that it may have been designed to hold brandy — is specially pleasing.

Thistle blend and Tobermory malt are two miniatures that have labels fired onto the bottles. Highland Park has a transparent label stuck on, to give the same appearance as the fired-on label of the 75 cl bottle.

Mackinlay's Legacy has an interesting label. The miniature is 'flat airline' but the label has been shaded in a way that gives the impression of the 'waisted' shape of the parent bottle.

One of the prettiest labels is on Cadenhead's Putachieside. Sadly, the original printing plates were lost and the re-issued label does not have the same quality as the old one.

Miniatures and Literature

Scottish literature abounds in references to whisky, but it would seem that our writers have not been interested in their national drink in small containers, so that we have to turn to an English author for a literary reference to whisky miniatures. Readers of Graham Green's *Our Man in Havana* will recall Wormold's memorable game of draughts with the captain of police. Miniatures were used for counters and the winner of each piece drank the contents. It was Scotch vs Bourbon and it was Scotch that, by losing the game, won the tactical battle.

The book was written in the late fifties and collectors may be interested in the whisky miniatures named: Cairngorm ("An unfamiliar whisky . . . it found a raw spot on Wormold's tongue"). Dimple, Red Label, Dunosdale Cream and Old Argyll are no longer on the market. George IV and Red Label are now export only. Only the 'unfamiliar' Cairngorm eludes identification.

Whisky miniatures themselves have little to offer by way of literary references. There is 'Robbie Burns' and 'Immortal Memory' and a slightly embellished quotation from Tam o'Shanter on the label of Uisge Beatha:

"Wi' tipenny ale, we fear nae evil;
Wi' usquebae, we'll face the devil."

'Own Label' Miniature Whiskies

The practice by which merchants and others have their own labels placed on somebody else's product is not widely found in the field of Miniature Whiskies. From its nature, this kind of miniature can usually be purchased only from the proprietor of the label. Some examples which may be found in shops are given below:

STORES

Harrods has two different blend miniatures which are sold exclusively at their Knightsbridge store. The Scotch House vatted malt miniature is similarly restricted in sale.

HOTELS

Craws Nest, Turnberry and Post House are three examples of labels issued by hotels. Some are not easy to come by.

Inverlochy Castle Hotel used to have a miniature of its 'Grand Reserve' but this is now virtually unobtainable.

STATELY HOMES

Glamis Castle and Hopetoun House both have a watchglass miniature of their blended whiskies and these can be purchased at some specialist shops as well as at the houses themselves.

Inveraray Castle has its own 'house brand' — Argyll blend, which is widely available.

Cawdor Castle's original miniature is no longer available but they now sell exclusively at the castle a blend, 'Thane of Cawdor', and a Speyside malt.

OTHERS

House of Commons blend is obtainable only at the Palace of Westminster. It is a most handsome miniature bottling.

APT: With the slogan 'The Fastest Dram on the West', this unusual miniature issued by British Rail is, like the Advanced Passenger Train, temporarily withdrawn. The label is in the shape of the train itself and being on a triangular Grant's bottle, is designed to be displayed on its side. British Rail also issues three other miniatures — High Speed Dram, Sweet Dreams and Speedlink Dram. These are used for promotional purposes only and are not available for purchase by collectors.

Miniatures Used for Promotion of Products Other Than Whisky

From their nature, whisky miniatures used for product promotion are not likely to be found in retail shops. However, the collector may come across samples from time to time and possession of them will help to lend distinctiveness to his display. Here are two recent examples:

Cashmere Blend

This label was issued by a firm of high-class yarn manufacturers as part of a larger package promoting a new venture into the manufacture of knitwear. The package contained a history of the old-established company and the whisky, in a flat tartan-pack, was inset within the package. This miniature is unobtainable.

Scotland's For Me

This is a case of Scotland promoting itself through its own most famous product. The Scottish Tourist Board has issued the label as part of its current 'Scotland's For Me!' campaign. Although the original flat bottling was never available for puchase, a new issue, using Highland Queen miniatures, is now to be found in shops in Scotland.

Miniature Whiskies as Souvenirs

There has been surprisingly little attempt to exploit Scotland's national drink as a souvenir, by issuing special labels. The reason is, perhaps, that any Scotch whisky miniature is a fitting 'minding' of a visit to Scotland and certainly many thousands are purchased for this purpose each year.

A few miniatures carry tartan on their labels: Clan Blend, Hielanman, Inver House, MacGregor's and Real Mackenzie are examples from the blends, but the garb of the two highlanders on the Glen Grant label  is almost the only example among the malts. Some miniatures are presented in tartan boxes; the best known are in the familiar 'Tartanpak' series.

The writer has in his possession a miniature stoneware jar which carries the message, "A Wee Deoch an Dorius from Braemar". As with many novelties on a miniature scale, it is the container rather than the unnamed whisky that carries the message.

Although any Scotch whisky may be a suitable souvenir, some brand names are specially appropriate; Thistle and White Heather are obvious examples, as are those carrying Scottish surnames. Other possible choices are:

Wild Life: The Monarch (of the Glen), Harts, Highland Mist, (all of which portray stags on their labels), Golden Eagle, Golden Beneagles, Famous Grouse.

Places: Isle of Skye, Royal Deeside, Ainsley's Royal Edinburgh, Tobermory, Argyll, Campbeltown Loch, Spey Cast.

The only example of Gaelic on a miniature label is, appropriately, Uisge Beatha, Water of Life. It is ironic that when this Gaelic expression passed into the English language, it was the first part, meaning water, that was adapted to 'whisky'.

Whisky Miniatures Issued for the Promotion of Whisky Brands

It is a firmly held belief among whisky marketing men that the bottling of miniatures is not in itself profitable. The primary reason for the issue of miniatures by the leading whisky companies is to help promote sales of their products in bars or through stores, in larger bottles; if they cease to exercise this function, they won't be issued, whether profitable or not.

Many standard blends first appeared in miniature form to help re-establish brand names in the U.S. in the period immediately following the repeal of prohibition. In this country the introduction of a new miniature often heralds the promotion of a particular brand. An example of this was the introduction of the new label Lang's Supreme when that brand replaced Red Hackle as the promoted blend of the parent company.

Whisky Miniatures Issued for Special Occasions

The wedding of the Prince of Wales was one of the first royal occasions to be commemorated by special miniatures. The most popular was the portrait miniature issued in at least three formats; the flat airline version can still be found in shops.

More unusual were the three malts issued in the 'Tartanpak' format by Gordon & Macphail. Glenburgie, Glen Grant and Strathisla were issued as vattings of whiskies distilled in 1948 and 1961, the respective birth years of Prince Charles and Lady Diana Spencer. These can still be bought.

Another sort of special occasion was celebrated in 1981 by Mr David Maund who put out a miniature whisky to mark his entry in the *Guinness Book of Records* as the owner of the largest collection of miniature bottles. This miniature is not available but information about it and similar issues can be obtained through membership of the Mini Bottle Club (see page 78).

Label Printing

A stamp collector who takes his hobby seriously will be
quick to recognise a stamp that has been issued just for
the collector. Having recognised its purpose, he will
probably reject it, preferring to collect only those stamps
that are genuinely issued for postal purposes.

Collectors of miniature whiskies may be faced with a
similar situation, where new labels (rather than new
whiskies, suitably labelled) are issued only because there
are collectors who will buy them.

Recently, two firms with a number of export brands
have released them in this country on miniature bottles,
presumably with the collector in mind. Another firm has
issued several whisky miniatures with joke names. All
these firms are of the highest integrity, with impeccable
connections with the whisky trade. A real problem may
arise if the practice is extended and collectors are
confronted with miniature bottles of whisky with as little
connection with the everyday whisky trade as the stamps
mentioned above have with the world's postal business.

A collector whose aim is to accumulate as many
different labels as possible is unlikely to be deterred by
these considerations, but such collectors are few. Others,
especially if their hobby is based on a genuine interest in
whisky, will be more selective in their purchasing. There
are sufficient miniature whiskies issued for promotional
reasons, as samples or as commemorative souvenirs, to
satisfy the collecting instinct in most of us. If, however,
one of these labels is acquired, there is compensation for
the collector who does not want to display it. He can
realise its value by drinking the whisky; there is no
consolation like this for the philatelist who acquires a dud
stamp!

Vatted Malt Miniatures

Vatted malts are mixtures of malt whiskies from two or more distilleries. Some experts condemn this kind of blend because the constituent malts, each being strongly and individually flavoured, clash with each other. Other experts claim the contrary, saying that by marrying the best qualities of several selected malts, you get a more acceptable taste.

The constituent malts in vatted bottlings are not revealed. One might speculate that Glentauchers, Dalwhinnie and Convalmore, all licensed to James Buchanan & Co., are likely to be included in Strathconon.

The four 'Prides' issued by Gordon & Macphail, are interesting in that they give an opportunity to taste vatted malts on a regional basis.

'Own Label' Malts

These are single malts issued as the bottler's own brand, without naming the distillery on the label, which makes it difficult to say anything about them. It is interesting to note that the original miniature bottling of Sheep Dip was identical to Glengarioch, except for the label. It is possible that some bottlings that appear to contain mixtures of malts are in fact single malts; for this reason, the two categories are listed together.

Single Grain Whisky Miniatures

The only single grain whisky marked in Scotland is Haig's Choice Old Cameron Brig. There is no miniature of this brand. The following two grain whisky miniatures are available:

North of Scotland (Cambus)   1964 57.1% – Gr Ro GS
The Three Scotches Grain   43%   – Gr Ro

Vatted Malts and 'Own Label' Single Malt Miniatures

Brand Name	Details		Shape & Colour		Note
Burn's Nectar	40%		Cl	Ro	
Campbeltown Commem.	12 yo 40%		Cl	Ro	24 diff. names
Cawdor Castle	40%		Cl	Fl	See P. 37
Cockburn's	40%	T	Cl	Ro	
Dalchully	15 yo 40%	T	Cl	Ro	
Dewar's Malt	12 yo 43%	T	Cl	Ro	
Dunglass	5 yo		Cl	Ro	
Glencoe	8 yo 100°		Cl	Fa	Highland Malt
Glenforres	12 yo 43%		Gr	Ro	
Glenmoriston	10 yo 43%	T	Cl	Ro	
Glen Saunders			Cl	Fa	Highland Malt
Grendel's	5 yo 43%		Cl	Fa	
Highland Fusilier	8 yo 40%	T	Cl	Ro	
Highland Fusilier	8 yo 60%		Cl	Ro	
Highland Fusilier	12 yo 40%		Cl	Ro	
Highland Fusilier	15 yo 40%	T	Cl	Ro	
Macphail's	10 yo 40%	T	Cl	Ro	Also TP
Macphail's	21 yo 40%		Cl	Ro	
Macphail's	45 yo 40%		Cl	Ro	
Old Elgin	8 yo 40%	T	Cl	Ro	Also TP
Poit Dhubh	12 yo 40%	T	Cl	Ro	
Pride of Islay	12 yo 40%		Cl	Fl	TP
Pride of Lowlands	12 yo 40%		Cl	Fl	TP
Pride of Orkney	12 yo 40%	T	Cl	Ro	Also TP
Pride of Orkney	12 yo 57%		Cl	Fl	TP
Pride of Strathspey	12 yo 40%	T	Cl	Ro	Also TP
Pride of Strathspey	25 yo 40%		Cl	Fl	TP
Real Mackenzie	8 yo 40%		Cl	Ro	
Royal Culross	8 yo		Gr	Ro	
Scotch House	8 yo 40%		Cl	Fa	
Sheep Dip	8 yo 40%		Cl	Ro	
Strathayr	12 yo 43%		Cl	Ro	Also Gr
Strathconon	12 yo 40%	T	Cl	Ro	
Strathspey	40%	T	Cl	Ro	

Using Malt Whisky Miniatures as Samplers

with Apologies to Glen Grant ....

The collector who is not a whisky drinker may be content to place his single malt miniatures on a shelf with the rest. The whisky drinker who enjoys tasting whisky's equivalent to the Château wines, will have a better use for them. He will welcome the increasing availability of these miniatures because they make it easier to sample the products of many distilleries without the expense of a full bottle, in surroundings of his own choosing.

Miniatures of Single Malt Whiskies: Introduction

Malt whiskies are distilled in pot stills, using no other grain but malted barley. Peat smoke is introduced in the malting process and this is one of the variable elements, along with the water source and the conditions under which maturation takes place, which gives each malt its individual character. When bottled on its own, without a mixture of grain whisky (which would make a blend) or other malts, this is a single malt or, in older terms, a self whisky.

Although many of the remarks in the following pages are addressed to the whisky drinker, the collector may find them helpful in broadening his interest in his hobby.

There are 116 malt whisky distilleries in Scotland. The product of 102 is now available in bottle as single malts and 83 of these can be bought in miniature form in this country. In contrast to the proliferation of blend miniatures world wide, the possible issues of malt miniatures is limited. In the lists that follow, the restriction to miniatures currently on sale in the U.K., applied to the blends, has been dispensed with and a full catalogue of single malt miniatures, whether available or not, has been attempted. In preparing the lists, the illustrations in James A. Triffon's *Miniature Bottle Collection, Vol 2, Scotch Whisky* have been invaluable (see bibliography page 79). Readers' suggestions for additions to the list will be most welcome, as information about earlier issues is not readily obtained.

Single Malt Whisky Miniatures — Explanation of Lists

DISTILLERY

The name of the distillery is almost always the name on the label, though there may be small additions, like 'The' (Balvenie, Glen Garioch, Glenlivet, Macallan) and 'Old' (Fettercairn and Pulteney).

AGE AND PROOF

As stated on the label. If known, but not shown on the miniature label, details are put within brackets. No entry is made if the age or strength is not known.

AVAILABILITY

++ Currently available in U.K. shops
+   Older issue, still available at the time of writing
-   Discontinued within the last few years and unlikely to be found in shops.
    No entry indicates unobtainable in U.K.

The figure in the second column is taken from Triffon's book (see page 79). It indicates availability in the U.S. at the time of publication (2 – Current, 3 — Different and Old, 4 — Old and Rare.

SHAPE,

Ro Round, standard tall
Rd Round, dumpy
Sq Square, tall
Sd Square, dumpy
Fa Flat, airline
Fl Flask, curved
Fs Flat, rectangular
Tri Triangular
Dec Decanter or decorative

COLOUR

Cl Clear
Bk Black
Br Brown
Gr Green

T   True miniature

TASTING GUIDE (See page 61)

NOTES

Cad Bottled by Wm. Cadenhead (page 58)
GM Bottled by Gordon & Macphail, standard bottling (page 50)
CC Bottled by Gordon & Macphail, Connoisseur's Choice label
TP Bottled by Gordon & Macphail, Tartanpak format

Malt Miniatures

Distillery	Age	Proof	Availability		Shape & Colour			Tasting Guide	Notes
Aberfeldy	1969	40	++		T	Cl	Ro	South	CC
Aberlour	12	40	++		T	Cl	Ro	Spey	New label
Aberlour	12	40	+		T	Cl	Sd		
Aberlour	12	43	++		T	Gr	Dec		VOHM
Aberlour	8			2	T	Cl	Sd		Italy
Aberlour	9	70		2	T	Cl	Sd		Also Fa
Ardbeg	17	46	++			Cl	Ro	Islay	Cad
Ardbeg	14	80	+	2		Gr	Ro		Cad
Ardbeg	10	(70)			T	Gr	Ro		Also Fl
Ardbeg	10	80				Gr	Ro		Pict label
Auchentoshan	5	40	++		T	Cl	Ro	Low	Buff label
Auchentoshan	10	43	++		T	Cl	Ro		
Auchentoshan	12	40	++			Cl	Fa		Dark label
Auchentoshan	(5)	40		2	T	Gr	Ro		Also Fl
Aultmore	12			4		Cl	Ro	K & E	
Balblair	10	40	++		T	Cl	Ro	North	New label GM
Balblair	10	40	++	2		Cl	Fl		TP 2 labels
Balblair	10	57	++	2		Cl	Fl		TP 2 label
Balmenach	1970	40	++		T	Cl	Ro	Spey	CC
Balvenie		40	++			Gr	Dec	Spey	3 cl
Balvenie	8	108.6	++			Cl	Fa		'As We Get It'
Balvenie	8	70	+			Gr	Fa		Also 75°
Ben Nevis	1965	40	++		T	Cl	Ro	South	CC
Benriach	1969	40	++		T	Cl	Ro	K & E	CC
Benrinnes	1968	40	++		T	Cl	Ro	Spey	CC
Benrinnes	23	46	++			Cl	Ro		Cad
Benromach	1968	40	++		T	Cl	Ro	K & E	CC
Bladnoch		40	++		T	Cl	Ro	Low	New label
Bladnoch		70	–		T	Cl	Ro		
Bladnoch	13	80		2		Gr	Ro		Cad
Blair Athol	8	40	++	2	T	Cl	Ro	South	
Blair Athol	8	70		2	T	Cl	Ro		Old label
Blair Athol	12	70		2					Italy
Bowmore	12	40	++	2	T	Br	Dec	Islay	
Bowmore	19	46	++			Cl	Ro		Cad
Bowmore	(8)	70		2	T	Br	Dec		
Bowmore	8	70		3	T	Cl	Ro		Ship label
Bowmore	13	80	–	2		Gr	Ro		Cad
Bruichladich	10	43	++		T	Cl	Ro	Islay	
Bruichladich		42.9	+		T	Cl	Ro		Also Fa
Bunnahabhain	12	40	++		T	Bk	Dec	Islay	In tube

The Age of Malt Whiskies

The age of most bottled malt whiskies is stated on the label. As whisky matures only in the wood, the age is that at the date of bottling. Whisky distillers consider that there is a certain age when each malt reaches a peak of maturity, after which that malt will not improve. The age may vary greatly from one malt to another but there seems to be a general agreement that Speyside malts reach this peak at about 15 years.

For the connoisseur, the age of a single malt may be of quite profound importance. He will tell you that two whiskies from the same distillery but different ages can vary significantly in taste. Indeed, he may discern between an eight year old and a 15 year old Glen Grant a wider variation of tasting experience than between a Glen Grant and a Glenlivet of the same maturity. The theory can be tested with these two malts, using available miniatures. Other age comparisons are suggested in the Tasting Guide (page 60 to 69).

Details of age are not always given on the label but the absence of this information does not necessarily indicate extreme youth. Some companies, seeking a wider market for their malts will value consistency of taste, obtained by mixing different ages of their malt, above commitment to a certain vintage. Examples of single malts with no age on the label are: Glen Grant, Glenfiddich and the new Balvenie.

The oldest whisky available in bottle is the 1919

Springbank which was bottled in very limited quantities in 1985. Less than two dozen miniatures were produced, with numbered labels. There have been bottlings of Macallan, Dalmore and Springbank at 50 years of age, in standard sized bottles. The only other prewar malt in miniature form is the Macphail's 1938 vatted malt.

48

Malt Miniatures

B C D F G

Distillery	Age	Proof	Availa-bility		Shape & Colour			Tasting Guide	Notes
Caol Ila	1969	40	++		T	Cl	Ro	Islay	CC
Caperdonich	1968	40	++		T	Cl	Ro	Spey	CC
Cardhu	12	40	++		T	Cl	Dec	Spey	New label
Cardhu	12	40	–		T	Cl	Ro		
Cardhu	12	43		3	T	Cl	Ro		France
Cardhu	12	43				Cl	Fa		Italy
Clynelish	12	40	++	2		Cl	Fl	North	TP
Clynelish	12			2		Cl	Fl		Italy
Clynelish	5			2		Cl	Fl		Italy
Convalmore	1969	40	++		T	Cl	Ro	Spey	CC
Convalmore	21	46	++			Cl	Ro		Cad
Cragganmore	1969	40	++		T	Cl	Ro	Spey	CC
Craigellachie	1971	40	++		T	Cl	Ro	Spey	CC
Craigellachie	20	46	++			Cl	Ro		Cad
Dailvaine	23	46	++			Cl	Ro	Spey	Cad
Dallas Dhu	1969	40	++		T	Cl	Ro	K & E	CC Also 1968
Dalmore	12	40	++			Cl	Rd	North	Also Fa
Dalmore	12	(70)	+			Cl	Rd		
Dalmore		70		4		Cl	Fa		Macbeth
Dalwhinnie	1962/3	40	++		T	Cl	Ro	Spey	CC
Deanston		40	++	2	T	Cl	Ro	South	Also Fa
Dufftown	8	40	++	2	T	Cl	Ro	Spey	
Dufftown	8	40			T	Cl	Ro		Old label
Edradour	1972	40	++		T	Cl	Ro	South	CC
Edradour	18	46	++			Cl	Ro		Cad
Edradour	21	46	++			Cl	Ro		Cad
Fettercairn	10	40	++			Cl	Rd	East	Also Fa
Fettercairn	(8)	70	–			Cl	Rd		
Glenallachie	12	40	++		T	Cl	Ro	Spey	
Glenburgie	20	40	++			Cl	Fl	K & E	TP R.Wed
(Glencraig)	1968	40	++		T	Cl	Ro		Glenburgie
Glenburgie	5					Cl	Fa		
Glendullan	12	47	++		T	Cl	Ro	Spey	New label
Glendullan	12	47	+		T	Cl	Ro		
Glendronach		70						K & E	TP
Glendronach	8				T	Gr	Ro		Samples
Glendronach	12					Gr	Ro		Samples

49

Glen Grant and
Gordon & MacPhail

The firm of Gordon & MacPhail has had a long and
distinguished connection with the whisky trade, in
particular as bottlers of fine malts. They were also
pioneers in the bottling of miniature Scotch whiskies. In
the thirties they bottled the first Glen Grant miniatures in
pear-shaped bottles, corked and capsuled. After the war,
they introduced the flask miniature which was later put
into the now familiar tartan carton with acetate front. This
'Tartanpak' range, purchased as souvenirs and gifts, has
introduced malt whisky into thousands of homes.

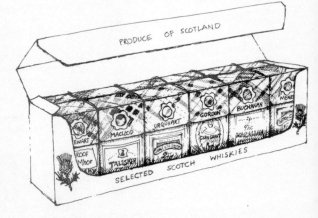

Gordon & Macphail have issued thirty of their
'Connoisseurs' Choice' bottlings in miniature form. The
malt enthusiast who uses miniatures for his initial
'sampling' can thus widen his tasting experience to
include Edradour — the smallest and Dalwhinnie, the
highest distillery in Scotland. He can decide whether
Caperdonich really is very different from its sister
distillery and near neighbour, Glen Grant. He can also
compare the product of the Lomond still (Mosstowie) at
Miltonduff with that of the original stills.

Malt Miniatures

Distillery	Age	Proof	Availability	Shape & Colour			Tasting Notes Guide	
Glen Elgin	12	43	++	T	Cl	Ro	K & E	
Glen Elgin	14	80	–		Gr	Ro		Cad
Glen Esk	12	40	++		Cl	Ro	East	
Glenfarclas	8	40	++	T	Cl	Ro	Spey	Boxed
Glenfarclas	21	46	++		Cl	Ro		Cad
Glenfarclas	8	40	–	T	Cl	Ro		Old label
Glenfarclas	8	70	–	2	Cl	Fl		TP
Glenfarclas	8	100	–		Cl	Fl		TP
Glenfarclas	8	105	–	T	Cl	Ro		
Glenfarclas	12	43		2	Cl	Fl		Japan
Glenfiddich		40	++	T	Gr	Tri	Spey	
Glenfiddich	22	46	++		Cl	Ro		Cad
Glenfiddich		70	–	2	Gr	Fa		
Glenfiddich	8	43		3	Gr	Fa		Old label
Glenfiddich	10	86	US	3	Gr	Fa		Old label
Glenfiddich	10	43		2	Gr	Fa		Japan
Glenfiddich		70		3	Cl	Tri		Old label
Glen Flagler		70		3	Gr	Ro	Low	
Glengarioch	10	40	++	T	Cl	Ro	East	
Glengarioch	10	40	+	T	Cl	Ro		In tube
Glengarioch		70	–	2	Gr	Rd		
Glengoyne	10	40	++	T	Cl	Ro	South	
Glengoyne	8	70	–		T	Gr	Ro	Old label
Glengoyne		70		2	T	Gr	Ro	
Glengoyne		70		2	Cl	Fa		
Glen Grant		40	++	T	Cl	Ro	Spey	
Glen Grant	12	40	++		Cl	Ro		GM
Glen Grant	12	40	++		Cl	Fl		TP also 8 yo
Glen Grant	12	40	+	2	Cl	Fa		
Glen Grant	18	46	++		Cl	Ro		Cad
Glen Grant	26	46	++		Cl	Ro		Cad
Glen Grant	12	57	++		Cl	Fl		TP
Glen Grant	20	40	++		Cl	Fl		TP (R. Wed)
Glen Grant	5	40		3	Cl	Ro		Italy also Fa
Glen Grant	8	70		3	Cl	Fa		Old TP
Glen Grant	8	100			Cl	Fl		Old TP
Glen Grant	10	70		2	Cl	Fl		Old TP
Glen Grant	10	100			Cl	Fl		Old TP
Glen Grant	16	80	–	2	Gr	Ro		Cad
Glen Grant	10	70		2	T	Cl	Ro	USA
Glen Grant	10	43		2		Cl	Fa	Japan
Glen Grant	12	43		2	T	Cl	Ro	USA

Glenlivet and
the Definite Article

When such things mattered more than they do today, the chief of one Highland clan declared that only three people were entitled to place 'The' before their name: The King, The Pope and The Chisholm.

Prefixing the definite article to suggest primacy is a device used to promote several malt whiskies. In recent advertising, Macallan has gone further and styled itself 'The Malt'. All right for Macallan, but when applied to lesser malts, 'The' has about the same connotation as 'Finest' has on the label of so many blended whiskies.

One distillery has gained recognition in law for a 'The' before its name. Smith's Glenlivet distillery had the distinction of being the first to take out a licence under the Whisky Act of 1823. Their whisky gained a great reputation in Victorian times and other distillers sought to share its fame by adding 'Glenlivet' to their own name. A lawsuit in 1880 failed to stop this but did win George and J. G. Smith the sole right to the title 'The Glenlivet'. The continuing use of the name by others, led to advertisements like this:

> "George and John Gordon Smith . . . beg to intimate that Glenlivet is a district which belongs to his Grace the Duke of Richmond and Gordon, and that their Distillery was the first and is now the only licensed Distillery in Glenlivet and that they are the Sole Manufacturers of 'Glenlivet Whisky'.

There are now two other distilleries in the glen and one, Tamnavulin-Glenlivet is bottled as a miniature. Seven other miniature malts have 'Glenlivet' on the label, so also has one blend, Glen Calder, which announces itself as being 'from the Glenlivet District'.

Glenlivet.

Malt Miniatures

Distillery	Age	Proof	Availability		Shape & Colour			Tasting Notes Guide	
Glen Keith	1963	40	–		T	Cl	Ro	K & E	CC
Glenkinchie	17	46	++			Cl	Ro	Low	Cad
Glenlivet	12	40	++	2	T	Gr	Ro	Spey	
Glenlivet	12	40	++			Cl	Fl		TP
Glenlivet	12	57	++			Cl	Fl		TP
Glenlivet	12	40	++		T	Cl	Ro		GM
Glenlivet	14	80	+			Gr	Ro		Cad
Glenlivet	18	46	++			Cl	Ro		Cad
Glenlivet	26	46	++			Cl	Ro		Cad
Glenlivet	8	70				Cl	Fl		TP
Glenlivet	8	70				Cl	Fl		TP
Glenlivet				3		Br	Ro		USA
Glenlivet	12	45.7		2		Gr	Ro		France
Glenlivet		43		2		Cl	Fa		Italy
Glenlivet	12			2		Cl	Fa		Japan
Glenlochy	1968	40	++		T	Cl	Ro	North	CC
Glenlochy	27	46	++			Cl	Ro		Cad
Glenlossie	1968	40	++		T	Cl	Ro	K & E	CC
Glenmhor	8	40	++			Cl	Fl	North	TP
Glenmhor	8	57	++			Cl	Fl		TP
Glenmorangie	10	40	++		T	Cl	Ro	North	In tube
Glenmorangie	10	70				Cl	Fl		Boxed
Glen Moray	12	40	–			Cl	Ro		New label
Glen Moray	10	40	–		T	Cl	Ro	K & E	Also Fa
Glen Moray	10	70		2	T	Cl	Ro		Old label
Glen Moray	8	40				Cl	Fa		Germany
Glenordie (Ord)	12	40	++		T	Cl	Ro	North	
Glenrothes	8	40	++	2		Cl	Fl	Spey	TP
Glen Scotia	8	(40)	++		T	Gr	Ro	Camp	
Glen Scotia	5	(70)	++	2		Cl	Fa		Was Ro
Glen Scotia	8			3		Cl	Fl		Old label Italy
Glen Scotia	12			3		Cl	Fl		Old label Italy
Glen Tauchers	5	40				Cl	Dec	Spey	France
Glen Tauchers	12	43				Cl	Dec		France
Glen Turret	(5)	75		2		Gr	Ro	South	
Glen Turret	8	43				Cl	Ro		Round label
Glen Turret	12	46				Cl	Ro		Round label
Glen Turret	15	46				Cl	Ro		Round label
Glen Turret	21	46				Cl	Ro		Round label
Glen Turret	8	43				Gr	Ro		Old label
Glen Turret	12	46				Gr	Ro		Old label
Glenugie	1966	40	–		T	Cl	Ro	East	CC
Glenury Royal	12	40	++			Cl	Fl	East	TP
Glenury Royal	13	80	–			Gr	Ro		Cad

More About Proof

If you have no hydrometer and no gunpowder, it may be handy to know another (safe) way of testing the strength of a spirit. There used to be a special container called a 'Proof phial', but a miniature can be used for the purpose. The method is to shake the bottle violently and observe the characteristics of the bubbling. Here are the results of an experiment carried out with miniatures of Macallan (chosen because this malt has the widest range of strengths among miniatures):

Between 70° and 75°
Little variation. Bubbles in the stronger sample slightly larger, but tiny bubbles persisting longer in the weaker one.

Between 75° and 80°.
Considerable difference in size with the larger bubbles remaining longer on the surface of the 80° but with tiny bubbles continuing to rise for about the same time in both samples.

Between 80° and 100°
Still bigger bubbles in the 100°, but the difference less than in the last comparison.

It is probably not significant that the 12 year old 80° produced greater and more prolonged bubbling than the 18 year old sample of the same declared strength.

Another interesting fact about proof is said to be applicable particularly to Highland Park. It appears that if you take this malt at 100° and, immediately before sampling, reduce it to 70°, it will taste better than the same malt bottled at 70° and taken neat. This has also been said of Talisker but apparently does not apply to all malts.

Some experts say that the standard bottling strength (70° or 40% vol) is too low for malt whisky tasting. Before the first world war, the practice had been to bottle at 75° (which is still the usual export strength) but the lower strength was imposed as a measure to economise grain usage and has remained ever since.

Malt Miniatures

Distillery	Age	Proof	Availa-bility		Shape & Colour			Tasting Notes Guide	
Highland Park	12	40	++		T	Cl	Dec	Other	10 cl
Highland Park	8	40	++	2		Cl	Fl		TP
Highland Park	8	57	++	2		Cl	Fl		TP
Highland Park	22	46	++			Gr	Ro		Cad
Highland Park	12	70	−	2		Cl	Ro		
Highland Park	22	80		2		Gr	Ro		Cad
Highland Park	8	70		2		Cl	Fl		Old TP
Highland Park	8	100		2		Cl	Fl		Old TP
Imperial	1969	40	++		T	Cl	Ro	Spey	CC
Inchgower	12	40	++		T	Cl	Ro	K & E	
Inchgower	12	70			T	Cl	Ro		Neck label
Isle of Jura	8	40	++	2		Cl	Fa	Other	
Kinclaith	1966	40	++		T	Cl	Ro	Low	CC
Kinclaith	20	46	++			Cl	Ro		Cad
Knockando	1973	43	++		T	Cl	Ro	Spey	Boxed
Knockdhu	1974	40	++		T	Cl	Ro	K & E	CC
Lagavulin	12	43			T	Cl	Ro	Islay	Export
Laphroaig	10	40	++		T	Gr	Ro	Islay	Tube
Laphroaig	1967	40	++		T	Cl	Ro		CC
Laphroaig	10	40	++			Gr	Fa		Also 43
Laphroaig	10	70		3	T	Gr	Ro		Boxed
Linkwood	15	40	++		T	Cl	Ro	K & E	GM
Linkwood	12	70	++	2		Cl	Fa		
Linkwood	15	40	++			Cl	Fl		TP
Linkwood	15	57	++			Cl	Fl		TP
Linkwood	25	40	++			Cl	Fl		TP
Linkwood	(12)	70	−	2		Cl	Fl		TP
Linkwood	(12)	100	−	2		Cl	Fl		TP
Linkwood	12			2		Gr	Ro		
Littlemill	5	40	+	2	T	Cl	Ro	Low	
Littlemill	8	40	+		T	Cl	Ro		
Lochnagar	1969	40	++		T	Cl	Ro	East	CC also 1970
Lochside	1965	40	−		T	Cl	Ro	East	CC
Longmorn	12	40	++		T	Cl	Ro	K & E	GM
Longmorn	12	40	++			Cl	Fl		TP
Longmorn	21	46	++			Cl	Ro		Cad

Malt Whiskies and Associated Blends

Macallan is rated a 'crack' malt by blenders but remains one of the few distilleries in independent ownership and without close association with the proprietors of a particular blended whisky. Glenfarclas is similarly independent, though this malt is said to contribute strongly to the taste of Glen Calder. Two other distilleries that are not part of a larger group but which have their own closely associated blends, are Tomatin (Big T) and Springbank (Campbeltown Loch and others).

The following is a list of some of the blends that may be associated with particular malts. The absence from the list of many of the better known brands, reflects the fact that few of the malts controlled by Distillers Company Limited are bottled as miniatures.

MALTS	ASSOCIATED BLENDS
Aberlour	White Heather
Auchentoshan	Cairns
Bladnoch	
Blair Athol, Dufftown, Inchgower	Bell's
Bowmore, Glengarioch	Rob Roy
Cardhu	Johnnie Walker, John Barr
Dalmore, Fettercairn, Tomintoul	Whyte & Mackay
Glen Elgin	White Horse
Glenfiddich, Balvenie	Grant's Standfast
Glengoyne	Lang's Supreme
Glenlivet, Glen Grant, Longmorn	Queen Anne
Glenmorangie, Glen Moray	Highland Queen, Muirheads
Highland Park, Tamdhu, Glen Rothes	Famous Grouse
Isle of Jura. Glenallachie	Mackinlay's
Balblair, Glenburgie, Pulteney, Scapa	Old Smuggler, Ballantines, Grand Macnish

Malt Miniatures

M O S

Distillery	Age	Proof	Availa-bility		Shape & Colour			Tasting Guide	Notes
Macallan	10	40	++		T	Cl	Ro	Spey	
Macallan	1967	43	++		T	Cl	Ro		
Macallan	1966	43	++		T	Cl	Ro		
Macallan	1965	43	+		T	Cl	Ro		
Macallan	1964	43	–		T	Cl	Ro		
Macallan	1963	43			T	Cl	Ro		
Macallan	8	43			T	Cl	Ro		Export
Macallan	10	70		2		Cl	Fl		TP
Macallan	10	100				Cl	Fl		TP
Macallan	10	70				Cl	Fl		TP old label
Macallan	10	100				Cl	Fl		TP old label
Macallan	12	75				Cl	Ro		
Macallan	12	80				Cl	Ro		Boxed
Macallan	16	43				Cl	Ro		GM
Macallan	18	80				Gr	Ro		Cad
Millburn	1966	40	++		TT	Cl	Ro	North	CC
Miltonduff	1963	40	++		T	Cl	Ro	K & E	CC
(Mosstowie)	1970	40	++		T	Cl	Ro	K & E	CC
Mortlach	12	40	++		T	Cl	Ro	Spey	GM
Mortlach	12	40	++	2		Cl	Fl		TP
Mortlach	12	57	++	2		Cl	Fl		TP
Mortlach	22	80	–	2		Gr	Ro		Cad
Mortlach	12					Cl	Fa		Export
Oban	12	(40)	++		T	Cl	Dec	South	
Old Pulteney	8	40	++			Cl	Fl	North	TP
Old Pulteney	8	57	++			Cl	Fl		TP
Old Pulteney	8	70	–	2		Cl	Fl		TP old label
Old Pulteney	8	100	–	2		Cl	Fl		TP old label
Port Ellen	1969	40	++		T	Cl	Ro	Islay	CC
Rosebank	17	46	++			Cl	Ro	Low	Cad
Rosebank	12	43				Gr	Ro		Japan
Royal Brackla	1969	40	++		T	Cl	Ro	K & E	CC
St Magdalene	15	80	–	2		Gr	Ro	Low	Cad
Scapa	8	40	++			Cl	Fl	Other	TP
Scapa	8	57	++			Cl	Fl		TP
Scapa	8	70	–	2		Cl	Fl		TP old label
Scapa	8	100	–			Cl	Fl		TP old label

Wm. Cadenhead's Miniature

Most bottling of single malt whisky miniatures is arranged directly by the proprietors of the distillery. Some others are bottled by authorised agents, like Gordon and MacPhail. A few have been bottled under merchants' own labels, without mentioning the name of the distillery (see page 42).

The single malts marketed by Wm. Cadenhead are rather different from the others, being purchased on the open market and filled into bottles of uniform appearance whose labels name the distillery of origin and its proprietors. Gordon & MacPhail's Connoisseur's Choice bottlings (see page 50) fall into the same category.

Although some of the independent bottlings may not be approved by the proprietors of the distilleries, they will be welcome to the connoisseur, as they provide a unique opportunity to taste malts at interesting ages and some not otherwise available.

The Cadenhead miniatures are well spread over the tasting areas and in themselves offer a considerable spectrum of tasting experience:

Islay	Ardbeg	14 & 17	Bowmore	13 & 19
Lowland	Bladnoch	13	Glenkinchie	17
	Kinclaith	20	Rosebank	17
	St Magdalene	15		
South Highland	Edradour	18 & 21		
Campbeltown	Springbank	17 & 21		
Other Islands	Highland Park	22		
North Highland	Glenlochy	27		
Keith & Elgin	Glen Elgin	14	Longmorn	21
East Highland	Glenury	13		
Speyside	Glen Grant	16 & 18	Glen Grant	26
	Glenlivet	14 & 18	Glenlivet	26
	Benrinnes	23	Dailuaine	23
	Convalmore	21	Craigellachie	20
	Glenfarclas	21	Glenfiddich	22
	Macallan	18	Mortlach	22

All the Cadenhead bottlings are at 46% vol (80° proof).

Malt Miniatures

S   T

Distillery	Age	Proof	Availa-bility		Shape & Colour		Tasting Guide	Notes
Springbank	5	46	++		Cl	Ro	Camp	
Springbank	8	46	++		Cl	Ro		
Springbank	10	46	++		Cl	Ro		
Springbank	12	46	++	T	Gr	Ro		
Springbank	21	46	++		Cl	Ro		Cad
Springbank	1919		+	T	Gr	Ro		Limited
Springbank	17	80	–	2	Gr	Ro		Cad
Springbank	5	80		3	Cl	Fa		Italy
Springbank	5	80		2	Gr	Ro		Italy
Springbank	8	80		2	Gr	Ro		
Strathisla	8	40	++	T	Cl	Ro	K & E	GM
Strathisla	8	40	++		Cl	Fl		TP
Strathisla	8	57	++		Cl	Fl		TP
Strathisla	20	40	++		Cl	Fl		TP (R.Wed)
Strathisla	8	70	–		Cl	Fl		TP old label
Strathisla	8	100	–		Cl	Fl		TP old label
Strathisla	10	70		3	Cl	Ro		
Talisker	(8)	70	–	2	Cl	Fl	Other	TP
Talisker	(8)	100	–		Cl	Fl		TP
Talisker	8	70			Cl	Fl		Old TP
Tamdhu	8	40	++	2	Cl	Fl	Spey	TP
Tamdhu	10	40	++	2	T	Cl	Ro	
Tamdhu	8	70			T	Cl	Ro	Old label
Tamnavulin	10	40	++		T	Cl	Ro	Spey
Tamnavulin	(8)	40	+		Cl	Ro		Also Rd
Tamnavulin		75		2	Gr	Ro		Old label
Tobermory		43	++		Gr	Ro	Other	
(Ledaig)	1972	40	++	T	Cl	Ro		CC
Tomatin	10	40	++	T	Cl	Ro	North	
Tomintoul	(8)	40	++		Cl	Fa	Spey	Was Rd
Tormore	10	43	++		Cl	Ro	Spey	
Tormore	10	43	++		Cl	Fa		Old label
Tullibardine	10	40	++	2	Cl	Ro	South	
Tullibardine	12	80			Cl	Fl		Corked
Tullibardine		70		2	Gr	Ro		

The current label of Tamdhu 10 year old has a pretty
picture of the Tamdhu burn, with the verse:

Now calmed in deep pools
to reflect softly on the day;
Soon to swell the tumbling
torrents of the Spey.

Tasting Malt Whiskies — Miniatures as Samplers

The purpose of this section is to help the person who has tasted only a few malts chart his way through the bewildering variety now available, using miniatures as the most convenient way to obtain samples. Praise for particular malt whiskies abounds in the 'connoisseur' literature and no attempt is made to add to it. The aim is to make it easier for the reader to arrive independently at his own 'Top Ten' list.

Tasting malt whiskies is not an activity to be carried out alone. The first requirement, therefore, is one or two boon companions with the same general experience of tasting.

QUANTITIES: One 5 cl miniature is ample for at least two tastings, if several malts are to be sampled in a session and if judgement is to remain unimpaired throughout.

TASTING GLASS: Any glass will do but sometime try one of the tulip-shaped sherry glasses which are similar to the blender's nosing glass.

WATER: A little water added before tasting is said to release the aroma. It is not necessary unless you want to weaken the whisky. If your tap water is likely to add taste as well, use a bottled water, like 'Highland Spring'.

REFERENCE MALT: To help comparisons, it may be useful to introduce one particular malt into most tasting sessions. Better to choose a run-of-the-mill malt rather than one with strong individuality.

NOTEBOOK: If you are serious about tasting, a record made at the time of sampling will be invaluable for future comparisons. Such a record may help in selecting a few meaningful descriptive words which may later serve as a defence against the extraordinary catalogue of tasting terms found in whisky literature.

Tasting Experience

It may seem odd to make suggestions about **how** to taste malt whisky, but these notes may be useful, even if only to help understand the fine distinctions drawn by others. The sampling of a malt is carried out in three stages:

Nose:
The aroma or bouquet. A sort of reconnaissance by sniffing. This is how the blender judges the whiskies he samples. (He might be hard put to actually taste 750 specimens of whisky in a day).

Palate:
The taste in the mouth where the flavour is decided. If a wine were the subject of the tasting, this might be the end of it and the sample might be spat out. Fortunately, there is a further stage in the tasting of malt whisky, which requires that the spirit be swallowed:

Throat:
After the warm feeling in the throat comes the 'aftertaste' or 'aftermath' — a reprise of taste, in which the expert may detect elements missed by nose or palate.

Tasting Areas:
The usual classification of malts into Highland, Lowland, Campbeltown and Islay leaves a disproportionately high number of malts in the Highland category. For this reason, the latter has been divided into six, so that we have nine tasting areas, as follows:

1. Lowland
2. Campbeltown
3. Islay
4. Other island
5. Northern Highland
6. Southern Highland
7. Speyside
8. Keith & Elgin
9. Eastern Highland

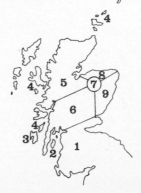

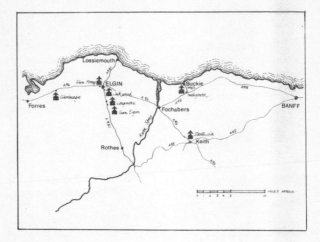

Keith & Elgin

Benriach, Benromach, Dallas Dhu, Glenburgie, (also Glencraig), Glen Elgin, Glen Keith, Glenlossie, Glen Moray, Inchgower, Knockdhu, Linkwood, Longmorn, Miltonduff, (also Mosstowie), Royal Brackla, Strathisla.

The Keith & Elgin distilleries are said to produce malts that have many characteristics in common with those of Speyside. A number of them still call themselves Glenlivets, a self-classification to be cautious of, being perhaps as unreliable a guide to taste as it is to geographical location. Longmorn is suggested as a 'middle malt' for comparison with others from the area as well as with those from Speyside.

The mixing of the ages of the two partners in the recent royal marriage in the special bottling of Glenburgie and Strathisla has no real significance in tasting terms, except that otherwise one cannot easily sample Glenburgie. In spite of the inclusion of 30 year old malt, it is Lady Diana's age alone that counts, to make this a 20 year old malt. The recent bottling of Linkwood at 25 years of age is a safer bet for sampling an older malt from this area.

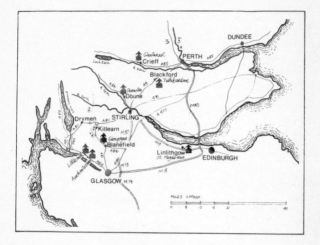

Southern Highland

**Aberfeldy, Ben Nevis, Blair Athol, Deanston,
Edradour, Glengoyne, Glen Turret, Oban, Tullibardine**

The characteristic taste of these malts is said to
reflect their geographical position between the
Lowlands and the Highlands proper, with bias
towards the former. Oban and Blair Athol are
exceptions, both being described as 'smokey'.
Confronted with a display of malt miniatures
many women choose to purchase Oban; the
shape of the bottle may perhaps suggest that
the contents will smell nice.

Lowland Malts

**Auchentoshan, Bladnoch, Kinclaith, Littlemill,
Rosebank, St Magdalene**

Some malt whisky drinkers scorn the Lowland malts as
being too slight for serious tasting. However, they should
be sampled; their lightness and alleged want of 'aftermath'
may in fact be very acceptable to the drinker who prefers
not to be browbeaten by his whisky — or by the pundits.

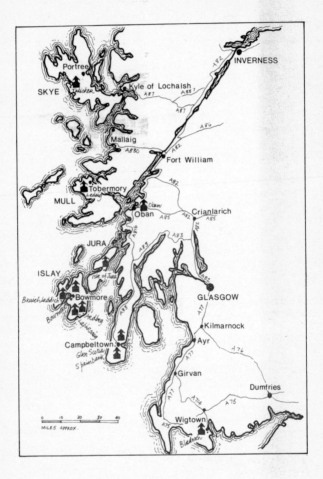

Campbeltown

Glen Scotia, Springbank

If the art of distilling came to Scotland from Ireland, then Campbeltown, only a few miles from the Antrim coast, is surely the birthplace of Scotch whisky.

There have been as many as 32 distilleries in the Campbeltown area when these malts were in great demand for blending. Economic depression and a failure to maintain standards led to mass closures in the late 1920s. Only Springbank survived in continuous production. Malt from this distillery can be tasted to two ages and the benefit of triple distillation (a process used only here and at Auchentoshan) can be judged. The whisky produced at Glen Scotia, revived in 1933 after a five year lapse, is said to be closer than Springbank to the Campbeltown malt of earlier days.

Isle of Islay

Ardbeg, Bowmore, Bruichladdich, Bunnahabhainn, Caol Ila, Laphroaig, Port Ellen

Powerful, pungent, full bodied, peaty, medicinal, tasting of seaweed, antiseptic, iodine — these are some of the words that have been used to describe Islay malts. Whatever you think of the distinctive 'Islay' taste, unless you have sampled and savoured the varied characteristics of these malts, you only half know Scotch whisky.

· Laphroaig ·

65

Kirkwall

Thurso

Wick

Clynelish
Brora

Tain
Balblair Glenmorangie
Dalmore
Alness

INVERNESS

Glen Mhor

Tomatin
Tomatin

Banff

Old
Meldrum

Glengarioch

ABERDEEN

Glenury Royal
Stonehaven

Fettercairn
Fettercairn

Blair Atholl
Blair Atholl
Pitlochry

DUNDEE

Perth

MILES

66

Eastern Highland

Fettercairn, Glengarioch, Glenury, Glenugie, Lochnagar, Lochside, (Glendronach)

The malts from the eastern part of the Highland area are reputed to be gentler than those of Speyside but more characterful than most of those from further south. Glengarioch has very recently been re-issued as a 10 year old and the miniature is accommodated in a tube container. Tasters may be interested in the following description of its eight year old predecessor: "The Glen Garioch has a magnificently robust rose, flowery, not very smoky; it is surprisingly mild on the palate, and it is this quality which could well become the Glengarioch signature". This example of tasting prose is quoted because it is less likely than most to influence the uncommitted sampler, not being taken from the report of a panel of malt whisky experts but from the bottlers' own publicity.

Northern Highland

Balblair, Clynelish, Dalmore, Glen Lochy, Glen Mhor, Glenmorangie, Glenordie (Ord), Millburn, Pulteney, Tomatin

The great difference in reported tasting characteristics between Clynelish ('full flavoured', 'like Laphroaig') and Glenmorangie ('fragrant', 'mellow') illustrates the drawback of grouping malts into tasting areas. Exceptions like this serve to remind us that every single malt has its own individual character.

Other Island

Highland Park, Isle of Jura, Tobermory, Scapa, Talisker

Like the islands themselves, these are malts of great individual character. Tobermory has not been widely available but the others all have faithful, sometimes sentimental, protagonists. Highland Park is available in three different strengths and its reputation when well matured can also be tested.

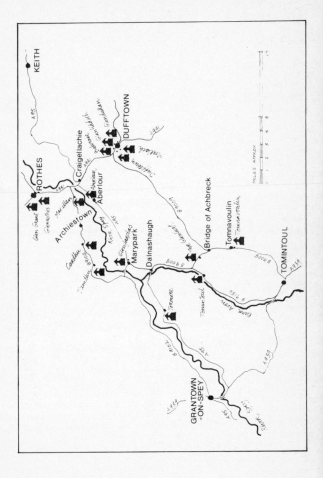

68

Speyside

Aberlour, Balmenach, Balvenie, Benrinnes,
Caperdonich, Cardhu, Convalmore, Cragganmore,
Craigellachie, Dalwhinnie, Dufftown, Glenallachie,
Glendullan, Glenfarclas, Glenfiddich, Glen Grant,
Glenlivet, Glenrothes, Glen Tauchers, Imperial,
Macallan, Mortlach, Tamdhu, Tamnavulin, Tomintoul,
Tormore

Although they offer a wide variety of tasting experience,
the Speyside malts belong together as a group, none
standing out strongly as having characteristics more
typical of another area. These are the classic malt
whiskies of Scotland.

One of the phenomena of malt whisky can be
experienced by sampling miniatures of Glenfiddich and
Balvenie; these sister distilleries, with common ownership
and drawing water and malted barley from the same
source, differ noticeably in taste. Both use stocks of
different ages in their bottling (age is declared on neither
label) but it is claimed for the 'new' Balvenie that use of a
high proportion of whisky matured in sherry casks has
influenced the flavour.

Through using miniatures only, a considerable range of
ages and strengths may be tasted. Balvenie can be
sampled at 108.6° proof (but presumably quite young)
under the 'As We Get It' label, while Glenfarclas at 105°
proof and eight years of age may be used to test the
theory that reduction to drinking strength is best done just
before sampling, by direct comparison with the undiluted
contents of the miniatures bottled at lower strength.

In commenting on the Speyside malts, it is difficult to
avoid reference to the high reputation of particular malts.
Let it be sufficient to say that malts whose water source
form part of the Spey river system are rated higher than
any in Scotland both by the connoisseur of single malts
and by the blenders who are responsible for the leading
whisky brands.

Jugs, Jars, Flagons and Flasks

It is not always easy to draw the line between miniature flagons, jugs etc., which can be related as containers with the whisky inside, and novelties, whose whisky content is at best incidental to the appearance of the container itself. In general, novelties are excluded from the listing opposite. Two borderline cases are the ceramic bell and the Golden Eagle, both of these are included because the miniatures have full-bottle equivalents, while both contain blends of whisky that are directly relevant to the container shape: Bells and Golden Beneagles respectively.

The Usquaebach miniature is rather an unusual one, being in the shape of an old two or three gallon storage flagon, rather than the usual pint jar. This miniature was made specially for an American outlet, but both it and the larger (600 ml) flagon may sometimes be bought in this country.

The Glendronach jar is sold only to callers at the shop in the distillery itself. The Glenfiddich flagon is also sold at the distillery Visitor Centre. Although this is a true miniature of the handsome flagon sold in export markets, the purchaser will have to fill it himself, as it is sold without content.

Older ceramic miniature flagons may sometimes be found in antique shops.

Miniature Flagons

Argyll	Black	Malt 12 yo 70° wax seal
Beneagles Dumpie	Cream/tan top	No label, Paper seal
Beneagles Flask	Green	Porcelain, eagle embossed
Beneagles Golden Eagle	Brown	Paper label
Bell's Ceramic Bell	Cream/brown	Label stuck on
Chequers	Green	Boxed
Eaton's	Black	DL Paper seal
Glendronach		At distillery only
Glenfiddich	Stone/green top	No stopper
House of Peers	Black	DL Paper seal
Kentshire	Black	DL Paper seal
King of Scots	Black	DL Paper seal
Langside	Black	DL Paper seal
McGibbon's	Black	DL Paper seal
Q.E.2	Black	Wax seal.
Rutherford's Plain	Cream/tan top	
Rutherford's Birds	Cream — 4 different printed designs.	Paper seal
Rutherford's Hunting Scenes	Cream — 5 different printed designs.	Paper seal
Springbank	Black	Malt 12 yo 43% vol. Wax seal
Strathayr	Cream/various tops	Paper label
Usquaebach	Cream/tan top	DL Paper seal
Whyte & Mackay and other proprietory blends	Cream/various tops	Paper label

Novelties and Curiosities

Visitors to Scotland will be aware of the many novelty containers of whisky that are offered for sale in tourist shops. These novelties vary greatly in quality but have in common the fact that the whisky content is largely irrelevant. Among the best of the figures are the animal models produced by Wades for Peter Thompson Ltd. of Perth, who fill them with their own Beneagles blend. Among the worst of souvenir novelties are glass containers of different shapes whose message 'A Present frae Bonnie Scotland' probably originated far south of the border.

 Peter Thompson used to issue 'The Thistle and the Rose' chess set, with pieces based on personalities from Scottish and English history. Collectors may care to assemble their own chess set. Here are some possibilities:

K. King of Scots, the monarch, King Edgar etc.
Q. Highland Queen, Queen Anne.
B. Abbot's Choice. (Ecclesiastics are not common on whisky labels and Bishop's Special is unlikely to be in many people's collections)
Kt. Sir Walter Raleigh seems to be the only knight but there are several horses: White Horse, Scots Grey and National Choice.
R. Glamis Castle, Argyll, Balvenie
P. Black Bottle, Black Douglas, White Hart, White Heather.

Another curious kind of small bottle on the market is the micro-mini. One firm in Scotland issues these and has the entry in the *Guinness Book of Records* to substantiate their claim to be the smallest bottles of whisky in the world. So far as we can ascertain, Spey Royal is the only label on a micro-mini that is not otherwise available as a miniature.

Whisky Liqueurs

There are currently on the market thirteen brands of liqueurs based on Scotch whisky. Nine of these can be purchased in miniature bottles:

ATHOLL BROSE
T Gr Rd 35% vol.

This liqueur has recently been re-introduced to the market by Gordon & MacPhail. This is 'Meg Dodd's' Dunkeld Atholl Brose and, oddly, since brose is essentially oatmeal mixed with milk or water, it contains no oatmeal.

DRAMBUIE
T Br Rd 40% vol

The most familiar of the whisky liqueurs, it is also the first to have been bottled. The romantic story of its association with the wandering Prince Charles Edward is told on the label.

GLAYVA
T Cl Dec 40% vol

Widely available, but much more recent than Drambuie, Glayva is said to have a similar taste. Among miniature whiskies, it shares with the 12 year old whisky marketed under the same name, the distinction of having a cork closure instead of the usual screw cap.

HOT TODDY
Cl Fa 28.5% vol

A mixture of honey and malt whisky.

LOCH LOMOND
T Gr Rd 35% vol

Another very recent introduction, it shares the same format as Atholl Brose, being in an identical bottle and having a neck label. A back label declares that "the sole base of this exquisite liqueur is 12 years old Scotch whisky".

Displaying Miniatures

Whatever its size, a collection of miniatures can provide a fine feature display. A small collection is easy enough to accommodate but as more are accumulated dusting becomes a problem and some sort of cabinet becomes desirable. Any glass fronted display shelving can be adapted but the purist wanting one to his own specification could seek a quotation from the firm of J. W. Shuttlewood Ltd. of Paglesham, near Rochford, Essex, who are specialists in this kind of work.

Only another 112 to go................

Lengths of 1½" x 1½" timber can be used to economise space in shelving. Six cut to the required length will give four tiers on a 6" shelf. This arrangement permits one to display about 30 miniatures per foot of shelf space, with a gap of a foot between shelves.

The Future for Miniature Whiskies

The whisky trade is never static and the supply of miniatures is always changing. Familiar labels may disappear but new ones appear to fill the gap. Collectors constantly seek out new labels and it is hoped the demand generated by this expanding hobby will help to persuade the whisky companies to further develop this aspect of their promotional activities. The more miniatures that are produced by the traditional whisky trade, the less scope there will be for those fringe operators who may appear on the scene to take advantage of the constant demand for new labels.

There are signs that an increasing number of malt whisky producers are aware of the benefits that can come from making miniature bottles of their products available as samplers. This will please the growing band of knowledgeable people who find malt whisky tasting an agreeable occupation and who would like to widen the spectrum of their experience.

One aspect of the miniature whisky trade that is likely to develop in the immediate future is the issuing of 'own label' bottlings. This will interest the more entreprising collectors who are willing to travel far in their quest for new labels.

Another development that may not be far away, is the greater use of plastic containers for miniatures. The problem of the plastic materials affecting taste, appears to have been overcome and trials have taken place in the airlines. A 'family pack' of six plastic miniatures has been issued by Whyte & Mackay (see p. 32). The lightness and less fragile nature of the plastic container will appeal to bottlers for economic reasons, but it may be some time before the drinking man can be persuaded to overcome the feeling that somehow plastic is not quite right for whisky.

Hunting Miniature Whiskies

Miniature whiskies may legally be sold only from premises that are licensed for off-sales. In Scotland, such licences do not permit sales on Sundays.

The miniatures listed in this book will be found in retail shops. Some of the specialised outlets are given opposite. Even these shops will not have discontinued brands in stock long after they cease to be issued. Indeed, one is more likely to find old issues in smaller shops, off the beaten track.

Two places where the miniature hunter is least likely to buy, are distilleries that do not have a Visitor Centre (and this means **most** distilleries) and the sales offices of blending companies. Even where distilleries have their own shops, it is as well to remember that their main business is to produce whisky, not to sell it in small bottles!

Another point to remember is that if you cannot find a particular miniature in a specialist shop, the supplying blender will have exhausted his stocks long before. Besides, even though they handle millions of bottles each year, a blender's own premises is itself unlikely to hold an off-sales licence.

A Mini-Whisky Hunter and Dog

When writing for information to a distillery or a blending company, or for a price list to a shop, it would be a courtesy to enclose a stamped addressed envelope for the reply.

Hunting Whisky Miniatures — A Buyer's Guide

Most off-licence stores stock miniatures of the popular brands only and few have malts other than 'Tartanpaks'. The traveller in Scotland will find shops with a good range of miniatures in most tourist centres but there are only a few outlets with really comprehensive stocks where you are likely to get knowledgeable help from the proprietor or his assistants. There follows a list of retail establishments which are known to offer a good service for the collector:

SCOTLAND

Aboyne, Aberdeenshire — George Strachan & Co., licensed grocers in the Station Square. Specialists with plenty of miniatures to choose from, including their own Royal Deeside, Uisge Beatha, Pheasant Plucker, etc.

Inverdruie by Aviemore, Inverness-shire — Cairngorm Whisky Centre has an excellent stock of both miniatures and full size bottles. Also tasting room, whisky museum and audio visual show. Open all year.

Edinburgh — Lambert Bros., Frederick Street, just off Princes Street. Old established wine merchants with strong whisky section and one of the best stocks of miniatures. Own bottling includes: The Monarch, Talisman, Old Highland Liqueur. Postal business welcomed.

Also in Edinburgh: The Whisky Shop, Waverley Market and Cadenheads in the Royal Mile.

Elgin, Morayshire — Gordon & MacPhail, South Street. Long established merchants and bottlers of fine malt whiskies. Good stock of miniatures in their shop, including their own numerous 'Tartanpak' and other bottlings. Early closing day: Wednesday.

Tomintoul, Banffshire — Two shops with good miniature selections.

Tyndrum — Clifton Craft Centre with a good choice of whiskies in bottles, as well as miniatures.

There are few miniature whisky specialists in England but the following have excellent stocks:

Blackpool — D. M. & D. Shaw, Bolton Street. Mr Shaw is an enthusiastic and helpful stockist of miniatures from all nations.

Lincoln — The Whisky Shop, Bailgate. Open 6 days 8.30 - 5.30. Whisky specialists with a very good selection of miniatures.

London —Harrods, Knightsbridge, now has a Miniature section in its wines and spirits department.

Mini Bottle Club

Collectors of whisky miniatures who want to keep up to date with changes may like to join the Mini Bottle Club. Details of the club, which issues regular newsletters, may be obtained by sending a stamped addressed envelope to: Alex Barclay, 36 Norman Avenue, Harborne, Birmingham, England, UK.

Further Reading

Throughout this book we have tried to emphasise the additional pleasure that may be gained by a collector if he develops his knowledge of Scotch whisky parallel with his purchasing. The person who buys for tasting will need no persuasion in this respect. The information given in this book has necessarily been limited and selective but there are many books available to help fill the gaps. A selection of these follows:

Moss & Hume: *The Making of Scotch Whisky*, James & James

This is an epic piece of research into the Scotch whisky industry, seen particularly from the point of view of the distilleries. The book is very well illustrated

David Daiches: *Scotch Whisky, Its Past and Present,* Fontana

The paperback edition of this wide ranging survey of Scotch whisky, first published in 1969, is still in print. The style is discursive and personal but it remains one of the most useful surveys of the Scotch whisky scene.

Derek Cooper: *Whiskies of Scotland*

This is the best reference for for the general reader, full of pertinent information and pithy comment.

Philip Morrice: *Schweppes Guide to Scotch,* Alphabooks

A comprehensive survey and directory of the present day industry with the emphasis on marketing.

Neil Gunn: *Whisky & Scotland* Routledge

Sir Robert Bruce Lockhart: *Scotch* Putnam

Two nostalgic views of Scotch whisky, both classics of their kind.

Scotland's Malt Whiskies Famedram

Scotland's Distilleries Famedram

Excellent guides to the malt distilleries, full of information and anecdote.

James A. Triffon: *The Whiskey Miniature Bottle Collection, Vol. 2 Scotch Whisky*

This American publication carries an illustration of every miniature of Scotch whisky available to the writer and is a splendid catalogue of the miniatures sold in the United States in increasing numbers from the time prohibition was abandoned in 1933. Obviously not an up-to-date record for the British collector but an essential buy for anybody wishing to delve into the progress of miniature bottling. Vol. 1 records whiskies other than Scotch.

Harrod's Book of Whiskies. Published by *Decanter* magazine.

An interesting record of a marathon tasting session by four experts in the field of malt whiskies. A much more selective tasting was carried out by the *Sunday Times* Magazine in 1981. This survey actually awarded points to arrive at 'excellence quotients' for the 20 malts tasted.